Potter Park Zoological Society
1301 S. Pennsylvania
Lansing, Michigan 48912

birds

TEXT: **X. PALAUS SOLER**
DESIGN: **J. OPISSO**

1st. Edition, April 1979
I.S.B.N.
84-7424-082-4

The very intricate process that led to the emergence of a group of vertebrates capable of flight originated from certain reptiles called Archosauria during the Jurassic period.

The requirements of flight made their physical characteristics quite homogeneous, with bodies covered with feathers, small heads, wings, light bones, viscera intersected by pneumatic sacs, which typify a light animal with a high level of functionalism.

The newly acquired control of the aerial environment opened up a series of possibilities which led to an ample diversification in this new class of vertebrates that have always enthralled men by their beauty and behavior.

Only a man like Javier Palaus, willing to live with these animals and spend the greater part of his life in the wild areas of the most diverse countries and continents, could sucessfully guide the reader throughout this wonderful world as seen through his camera lens.

Dr. Jacinto Nadal Puigdefábregas
Professor of Vertebrate Biology
University of Barcelona

OSTRICH

CUCKOO

SUN BITTERN

CROWNED CRANE

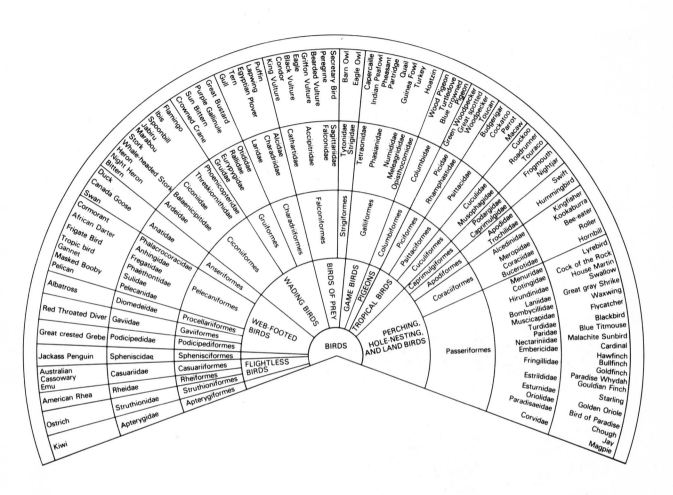

There are, at present, about 10,000 different kinds of birds. They were formerly grouped according to a systematic criterion based on the shape of their legs and bills, in the following groups: Flightless, Web-footed, Waders, Gallinaceae, to mention a few.

Modern ornithologists, however, have taken into account, not only the birds' external morphological characteristics, but also their internal anatomy and biology, thus creating new orders.

The following diagram shows the equivalence existing between these two methods of classification, as well as the family and order of the species mentioned in this volume.

PHOTO SAFARI

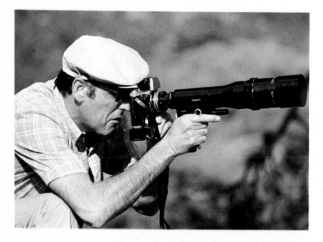

The first photographs of animals in their wild state were shot by the Kearton brothers in 1882. Their works were compiled in a book entitled "The Art of Surprising and Photographing Birds and Insects." They tried repeatedly to obtain good quality in their pictures.

Today, with technological advances, difficulties are minimized. Modern laboratories offer a wide range of film with diverse sensitivity; one can even obtain instant photographs by using Polaroid film.

Nature photography requires moderately specialized equipment. It is advisable to use a 35 mm Reflex camera, because cameras of 6 × 6 and 9 × 12 have slower shutter speeds and are more complicated to use. Their price is higher and they are somewhat of a nuisance when traveling.

The reflex camera should have a built-in exposure meter that functions with either slow and fast speeds including 1/500 and 1/1000 of a second. It is also best to have two camera bodies or a spare magazine that enables one to shot either black and white or color film, as the occasion requires.

Among the most reliable cameras are the Contarex, used by the photographer Eric Hosking; the Leika M-3, and the Nikon, used by the photographer Roger Tory Peterson, who also uses a 300 mm telephoto lens to shoot wild animals.

The Novoflex Company makes a very useful gadget that consists of a sliding focus handle which may be attached to any reflex camera. It comes with telephoto lenses of 280, 400 and 640 mm. This accessory has many uses in sports and nature photography.

When photographing animals at close range it is advised to use Kilfitt equipment which can be used at distances even closer than 2 m. If one desires to use larger telephoto lenses, an adaptor ring is necessary, although when using this ring, one cannot focus on infinity.

In order to obtain the best results when photographing animals in their natural habitat, the following steps are recommended:

— When the animal is in the distance, use a 500 mm or stronger telephoto lens.

— When shooting from a blind, use a telephoto lens of around 200 mm.

— Place the camera near the nest and shoot with a cable release or radio control. The photographer remains hidden at a distance watching with his binoculars. There are several cameras like the Nikon and Asahi Pentax equipped with a battery-powered motor which advances the film automatically.

HORNBILL

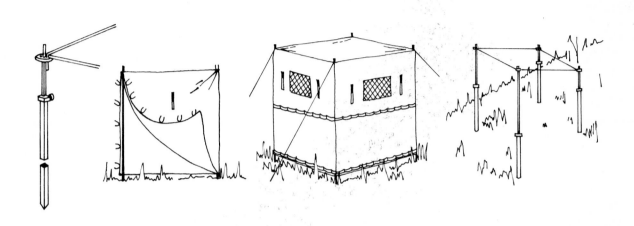

MIGRATIONS

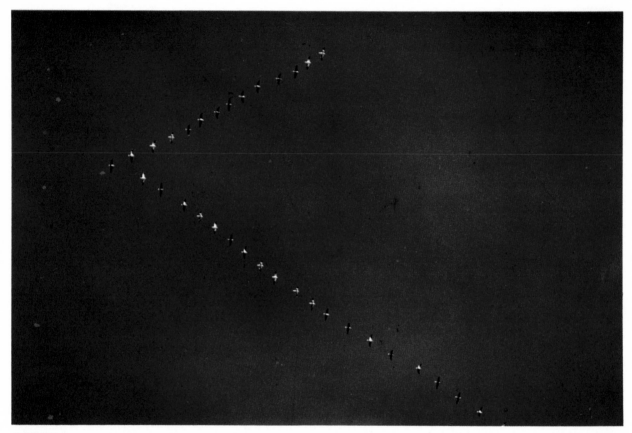

GOOSE

Migrations are one of the most interesting mysteries in nature, and a very common phenomenon among birds. Men was aware of these movements from ancient times. Only until recent times has it been possible to gather more precise information by banding birds as well as through studies of their physiology and anatomy.

After birds have bred in a warm area with harsh winters, they usually migrate to areas with a more benign climate. These areas are called "wintering areas" and the birds stay here until the next nesting season.

There are tropical species that migrate without leaving their habitat; but migration generally occurs from a cold area to a warmer one. There are birds that do not migrate to a better climate and cannot withstand winter weather maintaining their habits. The relatively few species in these circumstances are able to survive due to a hibernation-like slumber, called lethargy, as in the case of the Greenland partridge.

Migration cannot be considered as a behavioral characteristic of specific species of birds, as within the same species some members may migrate and others may not. Some birds migrate in large flocks, others in small coveys and still others migrate alone. Some of the birds that migrate in flocks form distinctive flight patterns. Specimens of different species can be found in the same flock of migrating birds. Some species fly in a straight line, across oceans and deserts. Others follow the coastline, and others the courses of continental waters. There are birds that fly both day and night; some fly only during the day and rest at night, and others do the opposite. Most birds, however, do not fly especially high when migrating. Most of the species of central Europe and Asia winter in South Africa, southern Asia and Australia, and follow fixed routes. The species from the north of the North American continent winter in Central and South America, and follow three main migrating routes: one runs along the

Atlantic coastline, another follows the Pacific coast, and the other the Mississippi River.

The distance of the migration varies according to several factors. It is not always the most powerful bird or best flier that embarks upon the longest flight. The Siberian nightingale winters in Africa after traveling 10,000 kms. The sea swallow nests near the North Pole and winters by the shores of the Antarctic Sea after a trip of 30,000 kms. The curlew flies from Terranova to Ireland in two days or even less if the wind is favorable.

"Most birds can also run, climb or swim, and this enables them to occupy even larger areas on Earth than mammals." (Herbert Wendt).

There are diverse theories about the origin of migrations, some of them even contradictory. Perhaps the most generally accepted theory is that which considers the influence of sexual hormones.

This theory is based on a series of experiments carried out by the Canadian zoologist William Rowan, who was able, by the use of artificial light, to provoke premature migrations in small Fringillidae birds during the winter.

Based on this experiment and others of a similar nature, it was concluded that sexual hormones, which are abundantly secreted as the sexual organs develop, induce the need of finding a suitable breeding site. Light stimulates the secretion of sexual hormones and consequently migration begins when the days are longer, also announcing the arrival of the warm season.

Contradicting this theory, other scientists have proved that birds whose sexual organs have been removed also

migrate. Thus, the origin of migrations still remains a truly intriguing mystery.

Meteorological conditions may delay or advance the start of a migration, but very seldomly stop it. During the migratory flight, the birds' sense of sight is very important. It has been proved that if the birds previously know the area over which they fly, their flight is much faster than if it were for the first time. It seems logical to assert then, that birds guide themselves by certain geographical references, as airplane pilots do.

"Birds have a mathematically guided organism; man can make a similar structure, with the same movements, though less powerful and with a lesser capacity to maintain its equilibrium. Such a man-made instrument would only need the birds' soul..." (Leonardo da Vinci).

"The instinct of flight resides in birds, but the desire is also akin to men." (Goethe).

On the other hand, the fact that some birds make long flights over the ocean casts a doubt on the theory that asserts that birds depend on their eyesight to guide them in their migrations. Some authors try to discover relationships between migratory flights and the position of certain stars and constellations. The truth is that birds possess a sense of orientation whose secret is stil unknown.

TERN

ABDIM'S STORK

NESTS

WHITE WAGTAIL

LAPWING

Once the courtship rite is over, birds begin to nest. Some are poligamous, like the Galliformes, the Gruiformes, etc. In this case, the male defends and guards the females but does not look after the nest or the brood. The birds of other orders, like the Columbiformes, Anseriformes, etc., live in pairs and both male and female remain together all their lives.

Most birds build their own nests, with the exception of some species that lay their eggs on the ground or use other birds' abandoned nests. The nidicolous species work tirelessly to build their nests. When spring arrives they choose a place and gather all kinds of materials to make a comfortable nest for the eggs. While incubating the eggs, the female gives up her freedom and will not leave the brood until they hatch. The new-born chicks rid themselves of the egg shell using a horny projection on their bills. Both parents continuously feed their offspring until they are able to feed themselves.

It must be kept in mind that to survive, birds need to eat the equivalent to half their weight daily all their lives. In

order to obtain a gram of food, the insectivorous birds must eat between 50 and 500 insects, depending on their size. The parents not only take care of feeding their fledglings but also protect them from possible predators.

Nidifugous species make very crude nests: they use any hollow in the ground and line it with shrubs. As soon as the chicks hatch, they follow their parents. From the moment of birth, the young try to peck at everything. These helpless creatures are protected by their subdued coloring which enables them to go unnoticed by their natural predators. In this manner the offspring remains safe while their parents face the foe.

Some species, like the grebes and divers make floating platforms of reeds and aquatic plants in a sheltered lagoon. If the parents leave momentarily the nest, they first cover the eggs with grasses.

Most birds, like the birds of prey, wading birds and common birds, nest in trees. The size of nests is quite varied: it ranges from the very small up to those measuring 2 or 3 m in diameter. The penguin lays its sole

NESTS

BLACK WEAVER

smooth wall. A nest made of this substance hardens when dry, and the swallow lays its eggs inside. These nests are collected in large amounts in order to prepare one of the most appreciated delicacies in Chinese cuisine.

The parrot and the owl do not make nests; they merely use natural openings or nests abandoned by other birds. The cuckoo has a very peculiar habit: it does not make a nest, nor does it incubate or cares for its offspring. The female lays its eggs in other birds' nests when the adults are away. She lays one egg in each of various nests, removing one of the original eggs. The new-born cuckoo pushes the other chicks or any unhatched eggs out of the nest. In this way the chick gets all the attention from its foster parents.

The weaverbird is a true master of the art of weaving. Its nest reminds one of a cupola whose mouth would be the entrance. This nest can withstand strong winds and storms without the chicks getting wet or the nest falling from the branches to which it is attached.

The republican bird behaves in a very interesting way when making its nest. The construction is collective and many birds take part. These nests, seen from a distance, resemble the roof of an Indian hut, but in reality they consist of many large, closely grouped nests.

The hornbill builds its nest in the hollow trunk of a dead tree. The chamber where the eggs are laid is large and wide although the entrance is small. The male hornbill shuts the female inside by blocking the entrance with mud, leaving only a small opening through which he provides the female with food until the time when the young are old enough to fly.

The woodpecker makes its nest inside the trunks of trees. It drills a perfectly round hollow with its chisel-like beak. The nest opens up inside to a spacious area, set deeply in the tree trunk in whose bottom the female lays her eggs. The bee-eater and the kingfisher make deep burrows in the ground or at the base of vertical walls, laying their eggs in a wide space. After breeding, some species lay a second clutch. When natural conditions are unfavorable and the nests are destroyed, some birds are also capable of laying a second time.

Incubation usually is begun with the laying of the first egg and its duration varies according to the species. The shortest incubation periods are found among common birds, approximately 15 days. The brush hen incubates her eggs for 60 to 73 days; the emu incubates for 70 days; the kiwi 80; the albatross 90 days, and the Californian condor incubates its eggs for 180 days.

egg on the ground and carries it in a ventral fold. The brush turkey piles leaves, grass and twigs in a huge mound 10 m long by 3 or 4 m high. On its concave top the female lays the eggs which are covered afterwards. As this vegetal debris ferments, the resulting heat incubates the eggs. When the chicks break through the shell they shake off all the leaves around them and once dried by the sun, they leave the nest.

The flamingo moulds mud into a vessel-like nest about 50 cm. high which hardens when exposed to the sun. Within its shallow bottom the female lays one egg. In this way the egg is protected in case the water level rises or if there is a flood.

The swift swallow nests in cliff walls. During the breeding season this bird's salivary glands secrete a large amount of a viscous substance, which, when mixed with regurgitated marine algae, forms a mass that adheres to a

PURPLE HERON
THRUSH

MOOR HEN

BLACK-WINGED STILT

GRIFFON VULTURE

BLACKBIRD

APTERYGIFORMES

KIWI

This order includes birds the size of a hen, with a robust body, a small head with a long, thin bill. The nasal openings are at the tip of the bill. The stout feet are equipped with 4 toes, very developed nails, the first of which is very short. Their feathers are evenly distributed. They are tailess. This order has only one genus, with three species found in New Zealand.

KIWI *(APTERIX AUSTRALIS).* All the species of kiwis live in small groups or in pairs. These birds are nocturnal; at sunset they begin to look for food, poking in the shrubs with their long bills in search of worms, mollusks and insects. During the day they remain hidden in holes in the ground or amidst the roots of trees. During the mating season the males fight violently among themselves to find a mate. The females build a simple nest on the ground where they lay one or two white eggs, which are disproportionally large in comparison to the size of the bird. Males incubate the eggs and look after the brood until the young can support themselves.

STRUTHIONIFORMES

The members of this order are among the largest existing birds. They can reach a height of 2 m. They possess a strong body, black in the males while in the females it is brownish. Both the head and the neck of the adults lack feathers. The legs are long and vigorous, bare to the thighs, and the feet have two toes, the inside being the larger. The wings and the tail are covered by large feathers. Although these birds cannot fly, they are fast runners that can outdistance the swiftest horse. This order presently includes only one family with one genus and one species. It lives in semidesertic plains and arboreal savannahs throughout the greater part of Africa.

OSTRICH *(STRUTHIO CAMELUS)*. The ostrich is a social bird that lives in rather numerous groups. Females usually group together in hollows in the ground when nesting. The egg of an ostrich may weigh up to 2 kilos (about 25-30 hen's eggs) and is about 10-15 cm, in diameter. The shell is very strong and can withstand weighs of up to 127 k. without breaking. The incubation period lasts from six to seven weeks. As soon as the peculiarly stripped chicks hatch, they walk after their parents. Ostriches have varied feeding habits, thought they prefer vegetal substances. However, they do not disdain insects or small vertebrates such as amphibians, reptiles and birds. They will also eat any object that attracts their attention, for instance pebbles, and metallic objects that aid their digestion and remain in the stomach. Ostriches usually live together in harmony with other animals, namely zebras and antelopes. In the group there is always one that keeps watch while the others feed. If any danger approaches they immediately flee to find shelter. When directly attacked, they hide their heads under their wings in an attempt to pass unnoticed.

OSTRICH

AMERICAN RHEA

This order is quite similar to the Struthioniformes, with the exception of their smaller size and their having 3 toes instead of 2. The birds of this order do not fly but are fast runners. The order includes the Rheidae family, with one genus and two species: the common nandu, and the American rhea, native to South America, ranging from Brazil to Patagonia.

AMERICAN RHEA *(RHEA AMERICANA)*. This
bird's body is covered with feathers, except for its legs. The wings are long and have abundant plumage. The upper part is dark gray, and the abdomen is light in color. The rhea is adapted to life in wide, open areas and plains with shrubs and grass. It lives in small groups of several females and one male. Mating begins during the southern spring. At this time the males fight among themselves and the winner chooses the females that will make up his harem. The male builds the nest and the female lays from 15 to 25 eggs. The male also incubates the eggs for a period of a month and a half. The nestlings hatch covered with white down with brown stripes on their heads, and after a few days will follow their father. Rheas have been avidly hunted using different methods. At present they are hunted from horseback. Attempts have been made to breed them in captivity in order to acquire their feathers, but up to now these efforts have been unsuccessful. Rheas, however, adapt well to life in zoos, where they readily reproduce.

CASUARIIFORMES
CERAM CASSOWARY

This order includes large birds, incapable of flight, but they are usually fine runners. They are distinguished from related orders (for instance the Struthioniformes and the Rheiformes) by the following characteristics: they possess strong legs with feet bearing three toes and the wings are very short. They are native to Australia, New Zealand and nearby islands.

This order is divided into two families: Casuaridae and Dromiceidae. The Casuaridae family includes three genera with numerous species: the Ceram, Salvati and Bennet cassowaries. This later is the smallest of the genus and is found in New Guinea. The Dromiceidea family has only one species: the emu or Australian ostrich.

AUSTRALIAN CASOWARY *(CASUARIUS CASUARIUS)*, The cassowary is a good swimmer, and its main characteristic is a distinctive horny skullcap, resembling a helmet. Its plumage is shiny black. The neck is bare and has deep colored caruncles. The cassowary's feet are strong, with the middle toe more developed than the others. This bird lives alone, in small groups, or in pairs. The female is much larger than the male. This bird is territorial and aggressive, especially during the mating season. The female makes a scant nest on the ground with leaves where she lays from 3 to 6 dark green eggs. The incubation, which lasts two months, is the responsibility of the father. At the moment of hatching, the nestlings are covered with down with long, black stripes over a lighter background. They are already equipped with caruncles and the horny helmet. This bird is omnivorous and feeds on fruits, seeds, small reptiles, mammals, birds, and invertebrates. Wild cassowaries lead a tranquil life, indifferent to their surroundings. If they are attacked they escape by running at great speed.

EMU *(DROMICEIUS NOVAHOLLANDIAE).* This bird lives in sparsely vegetated areas. It is omnivorous, its diet consisting of vegetal substances and small animals. The female builds a nest near a shrub on any uneven patch of ground. She lines it with grasses and leaves and lays from 8 to 12 eggs, and occasionally more. The eggs are dark green in color. The male incubates the eggs for two months. When the young emus hatch they are covered with a grayish down with black stripes. Their growth is quite rapid and are sexually mature after one and a half years. At present this species is diminishing in number as they are considered a threat to agriculture and are therefore being mercilessly hunted.

EMU

CERAM CASSOWARY

PODICIPEDIFORMES

GREAT CRESTED GREBE

This order includes the Podiceps, with several genera and about twenty species. Worthy of mention are the grebes and the divers, distributed all over the world, except in the Antarctic.

GREAT CRESTED GREBE *(PODICEPS CRISTATUS),* This is the largest representative of its family, measuring up to 50 cm. in length. Its neck is slender, the lower part silky and white, while the upper portion of the body is brownish-red. This bird lives around lakes and marshes with high, abundant vegetation where it dives in

search of fish, amphibians and small aquatic animals. It also eats sprouts. While eating, the grebe consumes large amounts of feathers in order to soften bony remains and avoid any harm in its intestines. During the mating season the grebe is easily recognized by the dark ornament that appears on its head, and by the spectacular dance it performs before coupling. Its platform-like nest is built above the water and is made of aquatic shrubs. The female lays from 3 to 6 white eggs, which she protectively covers with leaves when she goes in search of food. The eggs are incubated by both parents for four weeks. The chicks are active as soon as they hatch, though they are carried on their parents' backs for a long time.

RED-THROATED DIVER

There is only one family in this order, the Gaviidae, which has one genus with several species distributed throughout the Arctic region. The position of the legs is unusual in these birds, as they are set behind the breastbone, near the tail. This characteristic makes it difficult for them to walk. They are excellent swimmers and divers, being able to remain underwater for one and a half minutes. The body is large compared to the size of the wings. Although it is difficult for them to take off, once airborne they can reach speeds of up to 80 k.p.h. (49 m.p.h.).

RED-THROATED DIVER *(GAVIA STELLATA).* During the mating season, the usually grayish feathers of this diver become quite colorful. In the winter the plumage turns gray and white. At breeding time the birds go to the most northern areas of the northern Hemisphere, building their platform-like nests out of plants' shoots on lake shores. The female lays 2 dark, black-spotted eggs. Both parents share the incubation of the eggs for a period of three to four weeks. The nestlings are born with gray and white down. They grow very quickly and are able to fly eight weeks after they hatch. These birds feed exclusively on fish.

SPHENISCIFORMES

JACKASS PENGUIN

The birds of this order are marine and unable to fly as their bones are heavy and dense. Their wings are long and wide, with only one joint at the shoulder. They use their wings as oars, and their feet as a rudder. These characteristics make them fine swimmers both on the surface and underwater. The body is covered by dense plumage and a very thick adipous layer of fat that helps them to withstand very low temperatures. They walk erect, with rather clumsy movements. In order to move rapidly, they slide on their bellies aided by their feet. This order includes the Spheniscidae family, with six genera and about seventeen species. All of them are native to the southern hemisphere (Antarctic coasts, southern Africa, southern Australia and New Zealand) with the exception of one species found in the Equatorial zone, in the Galapagos Islands.

EMPEROR PENGUIN (APTENODYTES FORS-TERI).
This is the largest bird in this order, measuring up to 120 cm. in length. The head is black and the neck yellowish; the breast feathers are white, and the bill is long and curved. This penguin lives on the ice barriers of the Antarctic and on occasion may be found in Tierra del Fuego. It feeds on fish, crustaceans and cephalopods. Mating occurs in the winter and nests are not built. A single egg is incubated by both parents in twenty-hour shifts. They are so keenly devoted to the care of their young one, that at times they inadvertently kill him while fighting to protect him. This penguin is often erroneously confused with the Dodo bird of the *Alca impennis* species which used to live on the coast of the northern Atlantic but became extinct in the middle of the last century.

EMPEROR PENGUIN

JACKASS PENGUIN (SPHENISCUS DEMER-SUS).
This bird is very well-known as it is commonly seen in zoos. Its predominant colors are black and white irregular patterns along its body. This bird inhabits South African shores and nests on islands far from the coast. Mating begins in November, and a nest is built on a hollow in the ground lined with shrubs and pebbles. The female lays from 2 to 4 greenish eggs. Both parents share the incubation of the eggs for a period of four weeks. The chicks are constantly fed by their parents for three months. The tasty eggs of these birds were formerly sold in the markets of Capetown. Their flesh, however, is greasy and unpleasant.

ALBATROSS

The birds of this order are exclusively pelagic. Their most distinguishing characteristic is the position of their nostrils, which open externally in a pair of tubes near the base of the bill. As a result of this characteristic, these birds were previously classified as Tubinaria. Their body is strong with long, narrow wings. Three out of their four toes are webbed, the 4th is independent. The plumage is abundant and thick, and according to the species, the coloring ranges from light to dark.

ALBATROSS *(DIOMEDEA EXULANS)*. This is the largest pelagic bird, its wingspan measuring up to 4,5 m.

It is white with black wingtips. The feet and bill are yellowish. The albatross is found along the southern half of the Atlantic and Pacific Oceans and from the Tropic of Capricorn down to the Antarctic. The albatross can make long journeys across the oceans using air currents to soar higher or lower without flapping its wings. It is also able to glide in the midst of the most violent storm. At sunset it alights on the water and resumes its flight at dawn. Its eyesight is very keen and allows it to spy small and medium-size fish. This bird usually follows the wake of fishing boats eating discarded wastes. As it uses so much energy flying, it must constantly eat large amounts of food.

PELECANIFORMES

The birds of this order present varied aspects but share common characteristics. Their plumage is dense, the wings are large, and the aerial sacs are highly developed. The bill is long and strong, and the toes are webbed. They live near the ocean and freshwater. This order is divided into six families: Phaetontidae (tropic birds), Pelecanidae (pelicans), Sulidae (gannets and boobies), Phalacrocoracidae (cormorants), Anhingidae (darters), and Fregatidae (frigate birds).

PELICAN *(PELECANUS ONOCROTALUS)*. This bird has a large wingspread, white feathers and a yellow pouch and bill. The flight feathers and the posterior edge of the wings are black. During the mating period its plumage takes on a pink color. It lives in large coveys near lakes, rivers, and areas close to the coastline in southern Europe, Asia and Africa. When fishing, the members of the covey coordinate their movements in order to trap their prey. On the land the movements of the pelican are ponderous and clumsy. During the mating season they gather in large colonies near marshes. Its grass and branch nests are built near one another on the ground. The female lays from 2 to 5 eggs, and the incubation period lasts one month. The young pelicans feed on half-eaten fish which they remove from the inside of their parents' gullets. They reach maturity after three years.

MASKED BOOBY *(SULA DACTYLATRA)*. This bird is distributed over a wide geographical area. It lives in tropical zones of the Atlantic, Pacific and Indian Oceans.

GANNET *(SULA BASSANA)*. The gannet is a marine bird, with a wingspan of 190 cm. Adult gannets are white with black wing tips; young birds have dark plumage with white spots. This species is very gregarious, and is found along the North Atlantic and Mediterranean coast. The gannet feeds on fish which it captures by diving down from a considerable height. During courtship, gannets form flocks of thousands of birds along the coasts of the islands of Feroe and Orcadas, and Iceland, as well as along river mouths on the Atlantic coast of Canada and the United States. Incubation lasts forty days and the young grow very quickly.

WHITE-TAILED TROPIC BIRD *(PHAETON LEPTURUS)*. This is a medium-size marine bird

PELICAN

MASKED BOOBY

GANNET

PELECANIFORMES

WHITE-TAILED TROPIC BIRD

FRIGATE BIRD

FRIGATE BIRD

whose central tail feathers are as long as its body. The bill is orange. This bird is found along tropical coasts or in the open sea in the Atlantic, Pacific and Indian Ocenas. The tropic bird is a fine swimmer and is usually seen perched on the high masts of boats from where it sights its prey which it catches by diving down at great speed. The parents do not nest and the female lays 1 egg which is incubated by the parents for a period of one month.

FRIGATE BIRD *(FREGATA MINOR)*. This bird is also known as man-o'war bird. Its body is elongated and the wings narrow and sharp-pointed. During the mating season the male displays a red throat-patch of naked skin that can be inflated like a balloon. The tail is forked and the small feet are provided with strong claws. The plumage is dark. The frigate bird feeds on fish, and when hungry robs other sea birds, killing them at times. It usually perches on trees or stones, very rarely landing on the ground. Its nests are built in shrubs, trees, or otherwise above the ground. The female lays 2 or 3 eggs, and both sexes share incubation duties. The plumage of the young will attain its adult coloration after two or three years.

AFRICAN DARTER *(ANHINGA RUFA)*. This bird is very similar to the cormorant, but it has a longer bill, neck and tail. It lives in marshy areas and rivers in tropical and subtropical African regions. Some species are also found in America and Australia. It lives in rather small groups and usually perches in treetops. It is a strong flier and dives well to catch the fish which it swallows as soon as it surfaces. It also feeds on amphibians, reptiles and insects. During courtship it forms large rookeries and nests in trees. Usually 4 eggs are laid, and both parents share in incubating them.

CORMORANT *(PHALACROCORAX CARBO)*. This is a large glossy black bird. It lives along the coasts, lakes and rivers in the interior of Europe, Asia and Africa. It perches on rocks and trees with its wings half-opened. It is very gregarious. The cormorant swims and dives very well in order to capture fish which constitute its sole diet. It can remain underwater for over one and a half minutes. Fishermen in Asia have trained this bird for fishing, placing a ring around its neck so it cannot swallow the fish it has just caught. The birds mate in March or April and build their nests of grasses and twigs in trees. Sometimes they borrow other birds' nests. The eggs are pale blue in color and up to 4 in number. Incubation lasts for four weeks. The chicks insert their heads into their parents' gullets to obtain half-digested, regurgitated food.

AFRICAN DARTER

CORMORANT

BITTERN

NIGHT HERON

GRAY HERON

GOLIATH HERON

SHOEBILL

STORK

CICONIIFORMES

These birds have a very long neck and bill; their feet are also very long with the toes well-developed and either webbed or unwebbed. Both sexes display similar characteristics, although during courtship the males acquire ornamental plumage. This order is divided into six families with more than a hundred species: Ardeidae (bitterns, herons), Balaenicipitidae (shoebill), Ciconiidae (storks, jabirues, marabous), Threskionithidae (ibis, spoonbill), and Phoenicopteridae (flamingos), etc.

BITTERN *(BOTAURUS STELLARIS)*. This bird's plumage is light brown with dark stripes. The feet are green and the bill yellowish-green. It lives in marshy areas with abundant vegetation in Europe, Asia and northern Africa. The bittern is mainly nocturnal and crepuscular, feeding mainly on fish, amphibians and small reptiles. When breeding, the bittern makes a nest with reeds in thickly vegetated areas. Three to five eggs are laid, which are incubated for twenty-eight days. At this time the parents give forth a soft, low "coo" repeated several times.

NIGHT HERON *(NYCTICORAX NYCTICORAX)*. This heron is similar to the bittern, except that it is smaller. The body and the upper part of the head are blue-black; the lower parts of the body are gray. This bird has a tuft of white feathers on the occipital portion of the head. This heron is widely distributed. It nests in colonies around marshy areas or in trees near rivers. The clutch usually contains 3 or 4 eggs. It feeds on fish, insects and snails.

GRAY HERON *(ARDEA PURPUREA)*. The wings and upper parts of the body of this bird are dark gray, while the head, neck and lower parts are brownish-red. It lives on the banks of rivers and marshes in Europe, Asia and Africa. Its diet consists of fish, amphibians and the larvae of aquatic insects. It usually forms colonies that nest in seedy areas, and seldomly in trees. The nests contain 3 greenish eggs. Although this bird exhibits some diurnal habits, it is usually more active at twilight and during the night.

GOLIATH HERON *(ARDEA GOLIATH)*. This is the largest heron, measuring up to 140 cm. in length. It usually lives alone or in pairs on the banks of rivers and lakes with dense foliage in southern Africa, Madagascar and India. Fish, amphibians, reptiles and small mammals make up the diet of this heron. It nests amidst clumps of rushes and papyrus.

STORK

MARABOU

JABIRU

SPOONBILL

SPOONBILL

SCARLET IBIS

CICONIIFORMES

SHOEBILL *(BALAENICEPS REX).* This bird's plumage is dark gray, except the feet and wings which are black. Its bill is quite large and shaped like a wooden shoe. It thrives in marshy areas near the upper region of the White Nile in Sudan and Uganda. Its diet is made up of frogs, fish and snakes. Its nest is built with grasses and aquatic plants. Here the female shoebill lays 2 bluish-white eggs. It adapts well to life in zoos but cannot be confined with other species.

WHITE STORK *(CICONIA CICONIA).* This bird is 130 cm. long and has a wingspan of 220 cm. Its plumage is mainly white with black wings. The bill and feet are reddish. This bird is found in the southern half of Europe, Africa, and central and eastern Asia. It feeds mainly on frogs, toads, fish, small mammals and insects which the bird catches using its long bill. During courtship the male claps its mandibles together creating a rattle-like sound as a sign of its willingness to mate. It nests atop trees, roofs and chimneys, and the clutch contains 3 or 4 eggs which are incubated for one month. In August the young storks are ready to accompany their parents in their migration. Storks usually return to the same nest in subsequent years.

MARABOU *(LEPTOPTILOS CRUMENIFERUS).* The average length of this bird is 150 cm. The upper parts of the body are gray and the lower portions white. The head and neck are flesh-colored with scant plumage. A pouch-like appendage hangs from the neck. This bird usually lives near ponds, lakes, and rivers in tropical Africa. Its diet is made up of amphibians and it preys avidly upon lobsters. It is generally seen with vultures in search of carrion. It builds its nest in trees, and here it lays 2 or 3 white eggs. The marabou's lower tail feathers are eagerly sought after on the market.

JABIRU *(EPHIPPIORHYNCHUS SENEGALENSIS).* This bird is 150 cm. long, with a wingspread of 240 cm. Its plumage is black and white with metallic tones on the head, neck and tail. The bill is red, black and yellow. It lives near swampy areas and rivers in tropical Africa. Jabirus are alert, cautious birds that live alone or in pairs. They usually feed on aquatic vertebrates, amphibians, reptiles, fish and small birds and mammals. They nest in trees and the clutch contains 4 white eggs.

SPOONBILL *(PLATALEA LEUCORODIA).* This wading bird is about 80 cm. long. Its feathers are white, and the feet and bill black in color. It is distributed throughout Europe, Asia and northern Africa. This is a

SACRED IBIS

gregarious bird found in marshes and along the edges of lakes. Its diet consists of fish, amphibians, worms, and insects. It nests in colonies in shrubs, trees or on barren islands. The nests are made of twigs and lined with leaves. The female lays 3 or 4 white eggs with reddish spots. Both parents take turns in incubating and taking care of the young. The nestlings are able to fly after seven weeks.

SCARLET IBIS *(EUDOCINUS RUBER)*. This bird is about 65 cm. long and its plumage is scarlet red. It lives in coastal and mangrove swamps in Venezuela and Brazil. It nests in colonies with other wading birds and the females lay 2 blue and brown eggs. The incubation period lasts twenty-one days with both parents taking turns sitting on the eggs.

SACRED IBIS *(THRESKIORNIS AETHIOPICUS)*. The overall length of this bird is 70 cm. Its tail is black and the featherless head and neck are also black in color. The bill is curved. The feathers on the rest of the body are white, except the flight feathers which are black. This ibis is found in Africa and southeast Asia, near the shores of

lakes, salt marshes, and flooded plains. Its diet consists of insects, worms, small amphibians and reptiles. It nests with other species in shrubs and trees and the 3 or 4 eggs are blue with brown stripes. These birds were worshipped by Egyptians in ancient times, who even embalmed them.

FLAMINGO *(PHOENICOPTERUS RUBER)*. This bird is 130 cm. long with a 180 cm. wingspread. Its plumage is white and pink with red feet. The bill is curved. It lives on the Mediterranean coast, in Central and South America, in India, near the Persian Gulf, and on the shores of Lake Baikal. Flamingos nest in colonies near shallow salt water lagoons with sparse vegetation. They probe in the mud with their bills to feed on algae and invertebrates. The parents build mud nests where 1 or 2 white eggs are laid. Incubation lasts for one month.

LESSER FLAMINGO *(PHOENICONAIAS MINOR)*. This is the smallest bird of this genus. It lives in southeast Africa, Madagascar and India. It nests around Lake Nakuro. The female incubates her 1 or 2 eggs for one month. The world population of this species is estimated to be around four and a half million birds.

ANSERIFORMES

BLACK SWAN

The birds of this order are distinguished by a bill whose corny, fluted outer edge has the function of filtering food substances from slime and water. The tongue is a fleshy lump made up of cartilaginous tissue covered by a ephitelium with taste buds and fringed with corny thorn-like projections. These are water birds, well-equipped for swimming by their waterproof feathers. During the summer they lose their flight feathers and are only able to fly when these feathers grow again. Most of these birds build their nests on the ground, although some nest in trees. The nestlings are nidifugous and precocious. This order includes the Anatidae family which includes about 150 species.

BLACK SWAN *(CHENOPIS ATRATA)*. The swans of this species are classified between the mute swan and the black-necked swan. They inhabit the coasts and lakes of Australia and Tasmania. They are mainly vegetarian and nest on small islands in lakes or swamps. The 4 to 7 eggs are light green in color. Australian natives take advantage of the molting season to hunt the swans when they cannot fly.

MUTE SWAN

MUTE SWAN *(CYSNUS OLOR)*. This swan is 150 cm. long with a wingspan of 230 cm. Its plumage is white, the nasal bulge and the feet are black, and the bill is red-orange. It is found in large areas of Europe and Asia. Its diet is composed of plants and aquatic roots, as well as mollusks and insect larvae. Courtship begins in the winter and the birds mate between March and May. Their nest is made of twigs, algae and leaves, and is placed near the water. The female lays from 5 to 7 eggs in a period of 2 or 3 days, after which she incubates them for five weeks. Mute swans are monogamous throughout their lives.

BLACK-NECKED SWAN *(CYGNUS MELA-NOCORYPHUS)*. This swan is over 1 m long. Its feathers are white, except for the head and neck which are black. It lives in the southern half of South America. When weather conditions are harsh the swan migrates to the tropics.

CANADA GOOSE *(BRANTA CANADENSIS)*. This bird is usually grayish with a black head, neck and tail, and white feathers on the belly and lower side of the tail. This bird is native to North America, though at present

ANSERIFORMES

BLACK-NECKED SWAN

CANADA GOOSE

it has been introduced into Europe, except the Mediterranean area. It lives in marshes and along lake shores. During the winter it is seen near the coast. They fly in V-shaped formations. The female lays 5 or 6 white eggs which are incubated for about a month.

WOOD DUCK *(AIX SPONSA)*. This is a beautifully plumed bird. Its sexual dimorphism is clearly seen. It lives mostly in the United States, and winters in Central America. It obtains its food from the ponds where it lives. It mates in March and the female lays a dozen or so eggs on the ground with both parents sharing the incubation.

MANDARIN DUCK *(AIX GALERICULATA)*. This multicolored duck is native to Japan and eastern Asia. In the wild it nests in trees far distant from the water. At present this duck is bred in captivity in different parts of the world and is greatly appreciated as an ornamental bird.

MALLARD *(ANAS PLATYRHYNCOS)*. This is a very common species of game birds. It is about 50 cm. long and has a wingspan of 90 cm. It is widely distributed throughout the northern hemisphere, the Canary Islands, Ethiopia, India, Borneo, the Antilles, etc. This bird inhabits ponds, rivers and marshes. It feeds mainly on vegetal substances but also eats worms and mollusks. It mates in the winter and nests in March in bushy areas distant from its usual habitat. Six to twelve eggs are laid generally, and incubation period lasts for a month. When the female senses danger she pretends to be hurt, thus confusing the predator and luring him away from the nest.

PINTAIL *(ANAS ACUTA)*. This duck is native to the northern hemisphere. It journeys thousands of kilometers in its migratory flight to its wintering grounds in Sudan, Uganda or Nigeria. This duck is usually nocturnal or crepuscular. Its nesting habits are similar to those of the mallard.

SHOVELLER *(ANAS CLYPEATA)*. This duck is 40 cm. long. It lives in the northern hemisphere in marshes and shallow ponds with slimy bottoms. Here the bird can extract floating, edible particles with its large bill. Its diet is basically composed of seeds and plants. During the migratory season it lives alone, in pairs or small flocks.

WHITE-FACED TREE DUCK *(DENDRO-CYGNA VIDUATA)*. Also called whistling duck, this duck is widely distributed throughout tropical America, Africa, and Madagascar. A black stripe running along its entire body is a peculiar characteristic of its plumage. The sides are striated, and the back of the head is white. This duck walks erect.

SHOVELLER   WHITE-FACED TREE DUCK

WOOD DUCK

MANDARIN DUCK

MALLARD

PINTAIL

This order includes diurnal birds of prey. Their heads are strong, with a hooked beak with sharp edges. The legs are long, bare, or covered with feathers up to the base of the feet which have strong, sharp claws. The flight feathers are stiff and strong, allowing these birds to undertake long-range flights. The plumage does not vary between the sexes. These birds are predators and scavengers. They nest in trees or atop boulders; the young are nidifugous and hatch covered with thick down. They are completely dependant on their parents. The birds of this order are distributed throughout the world, except the Antarctic and Polynesia. The order includes more than 300 species divided into the following families: Cathartidae (New World vultures, king vulture), Accipitroidea (eagles, bearded vulture), Falconidae (falcons), Sagittaridae (secretary bird).

KING VULTURE *(SARCONHANPHUS PAPA).* Its name derives from the fear it evokes among other vultures, which leave their carrion for the king vulture when it approaches. It lives in tropical American jungles, from Mexico to Paraguay. Besides feeding on carrion, it also eats live, small vertebrates. These birds are fine fliers and use thermal currents to remain aloft a long time. They nest in trees and lay 2 white eggs.

CONDOR *(VULTUR GRYPHUS).* This is the largest bird in its order, with a wingspan of 3 m. It is metallic black with white wings. The male has a fleshy crest on the head; the flesh of the head and neck is wrinkled and featherless. The condor is the highest flying bird, soaring up to 3,000 m above the highest Andean peaks. It feeds on carrion but also eats small and medium-size animals. It does not perch on trees; its favorite habitat is among the highest mountains and cliffs. This bird lives alone or in small groups; however, when a corpse is large enough, many condors will gather together. The condor makes a large nest on a rocky ledge using small branches and lining it with grasses and feathers. The female usually lays 1 egg, very seldom 2, with both parents sharing in its incubation. The parents look after their young for a long period lasting over a year.

BLACK VULTURE *(CORAGYPS ATRATUS).* This bird is also known as turkey buzzard. Its plumage is mainly black in color with metallic tones. The head and neck are black and featherless. This bird is found from southern

KING VULTURE

CONDOR

BLACK VULTURE

IMPERIAL EAGLE

GOLDEN EAGLE   BALD EAGLE

United States to Patagonia. It lives in large flocks near roads and towns. It feeds on wastes and carrion and nests in trees, caves or in attics of abandoned buildings. The female lays 2 eggs and incubation lasts for a month.

IMPERIAL EAGLE *(AQUILA HELIACA)*. This
eagle is about 85 cm. long, with dark brown plumage; the upper part of the head and the skullcap are light yellow; the shoulders occasionally have white feathers. It lives in steppes and salt marshes of the Iberian Peninsula and eastern Europe. Its diet consists of mammals such as hares and rabbits, as well as partridges and aquatic birds. It mates in March or April, making a large treetop nest. At present this eagle is rigorously protected as it is near extinction.

GOLDEN EAGLE *(AQUILA CHRYSAETOS)*. This
eagle is slightly larger than the imperial eagle. It lives in mountainous areas of Eurasia, southern Africa, Arabia and southern Mexico. Its plumage is an even, dark brown. It catches its prey while flying just above the ground; it eats mainly hares, rabbits and various birds, as well as carrion. In March it builds a nest of twigs, grass and moss atop a boulder; the female lays 1 or 2 white, brown-spotted eggs which are incubated for forty-five days. The nestlings are fed by both parents and usually are able to fly after two

GOLDEN EAGLE

months. Sometimes one of the chicks kills one of its siblings.

BALD EAGLE *(HALIARTUS LEUCOCEPHALUS)*.
This eagle is 90 cm. long, with a wingspread of 2 m. The plumage is dark brown, except the head and tail which are white. It ranges from the Arctic to Mexico and is frequently seen along the seashore, or large rivers, and near lake shores. It builds a large grass-lined nest of branches and roots. The nest is placed in the highest branches of a tall tree, and the female lays 2 or 3 ivory-colored eggs.

SEA EAGLE *(HALIAETUS VOCIFER)*. The length of
this eagle is 70 cm. The head and breast are white; the upper part of its body is dark with metallic hues, and the lower portion brownish-red in color. It is found near rivers and lakes throughout the greater part of Africa. It feeds on fish, amphibians and aquatic birds; sometimes it also attacks flamingos and eats carrion. It nest in trees, bushes or on the ground and the same nest is used for several years. The female lays and incubates 2 or 3 white eggs; both parents, however, feed the young.

GRIFFON EAGLE *(GYPS FULVUS)*. This bird is
approximately 1 m long and its plumage is deep tan in

FALCONIFORMES

SEA EAGLE

GRIFFON VULTURE

color. The head and neck have a thin coat of down; at the base of the neck there is a necklace of light brown feathers. This bird is found in Asia, southern Africa and in the Meditarranean countries. It lives in cornices, mountain caves and cliff hollows. Its dwelling is easily recognized by the white remains of its feces. This vulture is a fine flier that glides using warm air currents. It can remain aloft for many hours without becoming fatigued. Its diet consists exclusively of dead animals which it discovers by the distinctive color of the crows and mocking birds which are the first birds to fall upon the corpse. The griffon's courtship flights begin in late January and early February. The nests are very simply made using any rocky hollows where the bird piles branches and twigs, later lining the nest with grass and feathers. The female lays 1, and very seldom 2 whitish eggs. The single nestling hatches in April and is fed by both parents; the fledgling leaves the nest in August.

BEARDED VULTURE *(GYPAETUS BARBATUS)*.
This bird is 150 cm. long with a wingspread of 250 cm. The upper part of the adult's body is gray-black, and the lower portion orange in color. This bird displays a characteristic black "beard" under its lower mandible. It lives in mountainous areas of northern Europe, Asia, northern China and northeastern Africa. It feeds on carrion and the remains of dead cattle, including the bones which the bird

drops from great heights in order to break them and eat the marrow.

PEREGRINE *(FALCO PEREGRINUS)*. This bird is
about 50 cm. in length. The upper parts of its body are light gray and the lower parts reddish-brown with small black patches. Two long black stripes origin beneath the eyes, running along both sides of the head to the neck. This bird has a very extensive habitat ranging throughout the northern hemisphere, Australia, South Africa, and Patagonia. It thrives in open areas, mountains and along coastlines; it also approaches cities. This bird flies very fast, achieving a velocity of up to 300 k.p.h. (186 m.p.h.) when diving. Its prey are usually birds larger than itself. This bird is greatly esteemed by falconers as one of the best high-flying birds.

SECRETARY BIRD *(SAGGITARIUS SEPRPER-*
TARIUS). This bird is about 130 cm. long, and its head displays a crest of feathers. Its plumage is gray in the upper parts, white below, and black on the flight feathers. The tarsi are very long. It lives in arboreal, brushy or densely vegetated plains in tropical and southern Africa. Its diet consists of amphibians, reptiles and insects. It nests in trees, the female laying 2 or 3 bluish-white eggs. At present this bird is zealously protected by law.

SECRETARY BIRD

FALCONIFORMES

BEARDED VULTURE

PEREGRINE

There are birds of varied size in this order. They have strong bodies with short wings and strong, thick necks. The head is small and in some species it displays a crest and caruncles. The plumage is abundant and sexual dimorphism is observed in most species. These birds are not avid fliers and have terrestrial habits. Their habitat is varied. Their chicks are precocious and nidifugous. Birds of great domestic and game importance are found in this order, which is divided into seven families with about 250 species. Among the families worthy of mention are the Tetraonidae (grouse), Phasianidae (pheasant, partridge, quail), Numididae (Guinea fowl), Meleagrididae (turkey), and Opisthocomidae (hoatzin).

CAPERCAILLIE *(TETRAO UROGALLUS)*. This is a rather large bird, 86 cm. long. Its coat is dark, the bill hooked, and the feet are equipped with little spurs. It inhabits conifer forests throughout a large area of central Europe, Siberia, and the Pyrenees. It feeds on berries, leaves and fruits. The mating season begins in April or May. At sunset at this time of the year, the male goes to a clearing in the forest and while fluffing its neck feathers and spreading its tail like a fan, it emits its mating call which also makes it easy prey for hunters. This bird is poligamous and when a female has been fertilized, she builds a nest under a shrub in the thickets.

INDIAN PEAFOWL *(PAVUS CRISTATUS)*. The male of this species is larger than the female and its plumage is more colorful. In the past this bird thrived in the forests and mountains of India and Ceylon, at heights of up to 2,000 m. Today this bird is distributed world-wide. Its diet consists of seeds, sprouts, berries, insects and small reptiles. The peafowl is poligamous and during courtship the male spreads its tail forming a beautiful fan. Its leaf-lined nest is built of small twigs. The female lays a clutch of 4 to 8 eggs and the incubation period lasts for thirty days. Females in captivity often abandon their eggs.

GOLDEN PHEASANT *(CHRYSOLOPHUS PICTUS)*. These are beautifully colored birds; the upper part of the head and the back are golden yellow, the lower part of the body is reddish. They display a tuft of very fine golden hackles on both sides of the head. Their natural habitat is the mountainous areas of Central China, and bamboo forests, 2-3,000 m. high. They are fast runners and do not fly much. They are often seen in zoos.

CAPERCAILLIE

GOLDEN PHEASANT

GALLIFORMES

COMMON PHEASANT *(PHASIANUS COL-CHICUS)*. This is a magnificent bird with a very long tail. This bird was originally native to western Asia but has been introduced into the United States, Europe and New Zealand. This terrestrial, quick-running bird thrives in forests with abundant vegetation. At night it perches in trees to escape predators. It feeds on fruits, seeds, sprouts, snails, worms, insects and small vertebrates. During courtship the cocks fight violently. The females scratch out a hollow in the ground under a shrub and line it with a little dry vegetation. The clutch consists from 8 to 12 greenish-yellow eggs and the incubation period lasts about four weeks. The young pheasants are very precocious and twelve days after hatching they are able to fly. This pheasant is a very popular game bird.

REEVE'S PHEASANT

REEVE'S PHEASANT *(PHASIANUS REEVE-SII)*. This is one of the most handsome pheasants. Its plumage is black and white and it has a very long white tail. It lives in the mountainous areas of northern and Central China. Its reproductive, feeding and breeding habits are similar to those of other pheasants.

RED PARTRIDGE

RED-LEGGED PATRIDGE *(ALECTORIS RUFA)*. This is a typical game bird, native to Spain but introduced into England, the United States, Canary Islands, and the Azores. It is a tranquil, fast running bird that can also fly fast though for only a short time. It lives in grain-growing farm country near brushy forests. During courtship the coveys break up and form pairs. They breed in May and build a grass-lined nest under a shrub. The female lays from 15 to 18 yellowish-white eggs with brown spots, which are incubated for twenty-three days. If the chicks are hunted by a predator, they scatter and huddle on the ground, passing unnoticed.

COMMON QUAIL *(COTURNIX COTURNIX)*. This is the smallest bird among the European gallinaceous. It measures only 20 cm. in length. Its is found in Europe, Asia and Africa. Quails migrate to Europe in April and return to their wintering grounds in September and October; some winter in southern Europe. They usually thrive in cultivated areas and their diet is made up of seeds, insects, and larvae. When nesting they scratch a hollow in the ground which is later lined with dry vegetation. Here the female usually lays from 7 to 12 up to 18 yellowish, brown-spotted eggs. Incubation lasts seventeen days, and sometimes females lay twice a year. The flesh of these birds is very tasty, and consequently they are relentlessly hunted.

COMMON QUAIL

VULTURINE GUINEA FOWL

VULTURINE GUINEA FOWL *(ACRYLLIUM VULTURINUM)*. The name of this bird is derived from its vulture-like head. Both sexes display similar characteristics. This bird is found in Somalia and Tanzania. It is a

tranquil bird, and at times it is found in large flocks in brushy, arboreal African plains. When startled, it runs to cover, rather than flying, flushing only at the last moment. This bird feeds mainly on seeds, sprouts, roots, bulbs and insects, as well as on small amphibians, reptiles and mol-

COMMON TURKEY

HOATZIN

lusks. The female lays about 12 eggs, incubating them for one month. Its flesh is greatly appreciated.

COMMON TURKEY *(MALEAGRIS GALLOPA-VO)*. The turkey gobbler has a series of large caruncles on its head and neck. It is found in the woodlands and open fields of Mexico and southeast United States. It is a poligamous and gregarious bird and it makes short-range migrations. During courtship the males fight among themselves. Turkeys feed on fruits, seeds and small invertebrates. They breed in April and May. The female lays from 8 to 15 yellowish, red-spotted eggs and incubates them for twenty-seven days. At present this bird is seldomly seen in its original habitat. The Spaniards introduced it into Europe in the 17th century.

HOATZIN *(OPISTHOCOMUS CRISTATUS)*. This bird is about 70 cm. long and is found in Brazil, Colombia, Peru and Bolivia. It forms large flocks that inhabit wocded, brushy areas. The females build a flimsy nest in low branches and lay 2 or 3 yellowish, brown-spotted eggs. The young are equipped with long toenails that allow them to climb branches. Hoatzins have foul odor.

GRUIFORMES
CROWNED CRANE

PURPLE GALLINULE

GREAT BUSTARD

The birds of this order are similar to those of the Ciconiiformes in their external characteristics, differing, however, in their skeletal structure and digestive tracts. Due to these internal differences, they were grouped in this separate order. They are agile when walking, but not fast runners. The foretoe is almost non-existing. This order has 10 families with 180 species. Among them are: Gruidae (cranes), Rallidae (coots), Otidae (bustards), Eurypygidae (bird of paradise).

CROWNED CRANE *(BALEARICA PAVONINA)*. This bird is about 1 m. long, with a characteristic black-tipped yellow crest on the back of the head. It lives in marshy areas in Africa in rather large colonies. It feeds on seeds, invertebrates, and small vertebrates. During courtship, crowned cranes.perform showy dances charac-terized by a fluttering of wings and hopping in circles around one another.

PURPLE GALLINULE *(PORPHYRIO PORPHYRIO)*. This bird is about 50 cm. long. Its plumage is a deep blue, with red bill and feet. It lives around densely vegetated lagoons in southern and eastern Africa, and it has also been seen in southern Europe. It is omnivorous. Its breeding habits vary according to its geographical distribution.

GREAT BUSTARD *(OTIS TARDA)*. This bird is approximately 100 cm. long, although the female is usually smaller. During the nesting season males display long, silky feathers on the lower part of the bill. Males are poligamous. The great bustard feeds on herbs, shoots, insects, and field mice. As its flesh is well-esteemed, it is widely hunted.

CHARADRIIFORMES
HERRING GULL

HERRING GULL

CASPIAN TERN

CHARADRIIFORMES

EGYPTIAN PLOVER

LAPWING

SOUTHERN LAPWING

This order includes mainly aquatic birds, limiculous, and of diverse sizes. They are good fliers and runners. They are widely distributed and their plumage is rather dull, without great differences between sexes. The nestlings are nidifugous and although only the female incubates the eggs, both parents share in feeding the young. This order is divided into 15 families with about 300 species. Among the families we can mention: Charadriidae (plovers, lapwings) Glareolidae (pratincoles, weaverbirds), Laridae (sea swallows, gulls, terns), Alcidae (puffins). Also belonging to this group are the jacana, woodcock, avocet, black-winged stilt, the Antarctic dove, etc.

HERRING GULL (LARUS ARGENTATUS). This gull is about 60 cm. long. Its body is blue gray with black-tipped wings. It lives in the northern hemisphere and is often seen along the seashore, near ports, and inland along large rivers. It is omnivorous but prefers fish, mollusks and crustaceans. It follows the wake of coastal ships. In February or March, the herring gull nests, laying 2 or 3 eggs. In the nesting colonies large numbers of young die because some adult herrings prey upon the young.

CASPIAN TERN (HYDROPROGNE TSCHEGRA-VA). This bird is gray and white, with a deep red bill. It is found in Asia, Africa, Australia, New Zealand and North America. It thrives in freshwater lakes and lagoons where it feeds on fish. Both parents incubate their 2 gray, black-spotted eggs. The young are able to fly one month after hatching.

EGYPTIAN PLOVER (PLUVIANUS AEGYP-TIUS). This bird is about 22 cm. long and lives in small coveys or in pairs along the banks of rivers, country roads, or near African villages. It feeds on insects and other small invertebrates; it also removes parasites from cocodriles, even venturing into their mouths to ear food residues. The female lays 2 or 3 reddish-yellow eggs with brown spots. In order to protect the eggs from predators, the female covers them with sand and feigns injury to confuse the enemy.

LAPWING (VANELLUS VANELLUS). This bird is about 35 cm. long, with white and dark plumage and some metallic green hues. It displays a crest of feathers in the rear part of its head. It lives in meadows and open fields in Europe and Asia; during the winter the lapwing migrates from northern and central Europe to southern areas. It mainly feeds on worms, insects and mollusks. It does not build a nest, and the female lays two or three eggs.

ATLANTIC PUFFIN

SOUTHERN LAPWING (BELONOPTERUS CAYENENSIS). This bird is about 30 cm. long, with plumage basically grayish with metallic tinges, except on the breast which is black and the lower part which is white. It presents a crest of long feathers at the back of the head. It is found in Central and South America in humid, marshy areas. Its diet consists of insects and other small invertebrates.

ATLANTIC PUFFIN (FRATERCULATA ARTI-CA(. This bird is 30 cm. long and has a wingspread of 60 cm. Its bill is gray, yellow and red. This bird inhabits the Mediterranean Sea and northern Atlantic coasts of America and Europe. It walks erect, and also swims and dives expertly. It feeds on fish, mollusks and crustaceans. During March and April it forms large colonies at its nesting grounds, sometimes using rabbit dens or digging burrows of its own where females lay only one white, brown-spotted egg. The female incubates this egg over forty days. Both parents feed the chicks and, in August when the young can fly the young birds leave the colony.

COLUMBIFORMES
GANGA

WOOD PIGEON

TURTLEDOVE

The birds of this order have strong wings, small heads, weak bills and short feet with well-developed toes. This order includes two families: Pteroclicidae and Columbidae. The Pteroclicidae are terrestrial and strong fliers; their tarsi are covered with feathers. They lay their eggs on the ground and do not make nests. Their young are nidifugous. All the species in this family are gregarious and dull in color. They are found in steppes and desertic areas of Africa, Asia and southern Europe. This family has two genera with seventeen species. Worthy of mention are the sandgrouse.

The Columbidae, namely the doves, turtledoves and crowned pigeons, are distinguished by a soft bulge on the upper part of the bill near the nostrils. They nest in trees. The young are helpless and feed on the so-called "pigeon milk," a milky substance secreted by the walls of their parents' crops. Some species are migratory. This family is very diverse, with about 250 species distributed worldwide, excepts at the poles.

BLUE-CROWNED PIGEON

GANGA *(ERIMIALECTOR QUADRICINCTUS).* This bird is common throughout Ethiopia. It lives in vegetated plains with low shrubs, as well as in cultivated areas. Its diet consists of seeds and roots. This bird does not make a nest and the female lays 2 or 3 eggs. It is a fast flier, traveling over hundreds of kilometers in search of water, which it must constantly drink.

WOOD PIGEON *(COLUMBA PALUMBUS).* This bird is approximately 45 cm. long, with a grayish head, and white patches on the wings and neck. It lives in densely forested areas and cultivated fields in Europe, western Asia and northern Africa. This pigeon is also seen in tree-filled city parks. Seeds and sprouts are its staple foods. Nesting time begins in April and the nests are built in trees. The female can lay eggs up to three times a year. In the winter they gather in large flocks with other species of pigeons. Its flesh is keenly appreciated.

TURTLEDOVE *(STREPTOPELIA TURTUR).* This dove is smaller in size than the wood pigeon. It lives in grain-growing or vegetated areas in Europe, western Asia and northern Africa. This bird lives in pairs or small flocks and eats seeds, sprouts and insects. The fragile twig and grass lined nest is built in trees. The eggs are incubated for fourteen days and the female can lay twice a year. It is a swift flier.

BLUE-CROWNED PIGEON *(GOURA CRISTATA).* This bird displays a colorful fan-like crest on its head. The upper part of its body is gray, and the lower part is reddish in color. The wings have a blue stripe, and the tail a white one. The feet are long and strong. This pigeon lives in New Guinea and nearby islands. It feeds on vegetal substances. It adapts easily to different climates and life in zoos.

PSITTACIFORMES
MACAW

PSITTACIFORMES

These are tree-dwelling birds, with large heads and short necks. The upper part of the beak is joined to the frontal bone of the skull; the lower part of the beak is shorter and overbitten. The feet are very agile, with 2 toes pointing forward and 2 backward. These birds are brightly colored and they live in dead trees where they make deep burrows. The females usually lay and incubate from 2 to 4 white eggs and the young hatch quite helpless. The birds of this order adapt well to life in captivity and live for a long time. The order has one family, the Psittacidae, with more than 300 species native to tropical and subtropical areas. The most colorful species are found in South America and Australia.

BLUE MACAW (ANADORRHYNCUS HYACINTHUS). This bird is 86 cm. long, with an overall blue coloration. It is native to Brazil and is highly-esteemed as a decorative bird.

RED MACAW (Ara macao). The red macaw is 90 cm. long, with red plumage, except at the base of the tail and wings which are blue. This bird is predominantly found from Central America to Bolivia.

YELLOW-BREASTED MACAW (ARA ARARAUNA). This macaw is 80 cm. long. The upper parts of its body are blue, and the lower yellow in color. It is found from Panama to Argentina.

RED-FRONTED AMAZON (AMAZONA FESTIVA). This parrot is about 35 cm. long, and is native to Brazil. The plumage is usually green, except the forehead which is red and the feathers of the edge of the wings which are sky blue in color. The name "parrot" is given to this species which possesses a long tail and inhabits Central and South America.

WHITE COCKATOO (CACUTUA GALERITA). This bird is entirely white, except for a yellow crest. It lives in arboreal areas near rivers in Australia, New Zealand and Tasmania. It lives in pairs or large flocks. Its diet consists of seeds, sprouts and roots. It nests in old trees in November and the female lays 2 white eggs. It is a menace to corn fields.

BLUE MACAW

RED-FRONTED AMAZON

KEA

PSITTACIFORMES

BUDGERIGAR

BUDGERIGAR *(MELOPSITTACUS UNDULATUS).*
This bird has adapted to life in all climates as a caged bird.
The original color of this bird in its natural habitat is green,
but diverse tones have been bred. It lives in Australia.

KEA *(NESTOR NOTABILIS).* The length of this bird is 48
cm. The upper part of the beak is long and sharp; its plumage is olive green with black-bordered wings. It lives in
New Zealand. Its diet consists of fruits and wastes. It was
necessary to kill many of these birds as they were a threat
to cattle. The kea would alight on the backs of sheep and
pluck out the fat surrounding the sheep's kidneys.

COCKATOO

CUCULIFORMES

This order includes medium-size birds with sparse plumage and a moderately long tail. The feet have 4 toes, two pointing forward and two backward. These are arboreal birds and some are parasitic, as they lay their eggs in other birds' nests. The order includes two families: Cuculidae (cuckoos, roadrunners) and Musophagi (touracos). The Cuculidae are parasitic species that are somewhat similar to birds of prey. This family is divided into 40 genera with 130 species distributed throughout all the continents. Some are migratory. The Musophagi are native to Ethiopia. They can dexteriously place their 4th toe next to the thumb. The nestlings display rudimentary nails near the carpus which later disappear. This family has about 15 species.

CUCKOO *(CUCULUS CARAUS)*. The upper parts of this bird are gray, and the lower portions white with dark stripes. It lives in diverse European, Asian and African habitats. Its diet consists of insect larvae, mainly caterpillars with hair capable of stinging. Its nesting is parasitic, with the female laying from 6 to 20 eggs beginning in May. When the female cuckoo lays one egg in a nest, she removes one of the original eggs in order to allow her egg to pass unnoticed. The foster parents incubate this egg for about thirteen days. As soon at it hatches, the young cuckoo expels the other nestlings, in this way securing abundant food for himself. The young bird leaves the nest 3 weeks after when it is able to fly.

TOURACO

TOURACO *(TOURACO LEUCOLOPHUS)*. This bird is extremely beautiful and colorful. It lives in pairs or small flocks in trees and in densely vegetated areas in the Ethiopic region. It feeds on fruits. This bird imitates the calls of other birds and mammals.

ROADRUNNER *(GEOCOCCYX CALIFORNIA)*. The length of this bird is of 70 cm. with the tail comprising 30 cm. This bird is also known as the terrestrial cuckoo. It is grayish-brown with white patches. It has a crest with erectile feathers on its head. It inhabits desert and steppe areas in Mexico and southern United States. Reptiles, such as lizards and snakes, as well as insects and spiders are its staple foods. In April or May it builds a nest in the lower branches of trees using diverse materials such as molted snake skins, papers, leaves, grasses, etc. The female lays 4 or 6 yellowish-white eggs which are incubated for nineteen days.

ROADRUNNER

STRIGIFORMES

EAGLE OWL

These birds have nocturnal habits. Their heads are quite large and mobile. The eyes are set in the front of the head and are surrounded by circular patches. The auditory canal is hidden beneath the plumage. These birds are yellowish, brownish, or dark in color. Some species have stiff feathers atop the head that resemble small horns. Their soft plumage enables them to fly very silently. Their diet is made up of alive small or medium-size prey, such as mammals and birds, which they eat whole. Later they regurgitate a pellet-like mass of hair, feathers and bones which they cannot digest. This order is divided into two families: Strigidae (owls), and Titonidae (barn owls), with more than 130 species distributed world-wide.

EAGLE OWL *(BUBO BUBO).* This owl is about 70 cm. in length, with large orange eyes. Its plumage is yellowish with dark stripes. It lives in Eurasia and northern Africa. During the day it remains hidden among stones and in caves or dens. It feeds on squirrels, hares, rabbits, partridges and all species of birds. Eagle owls bravely face their enemies, with ruffled feathers and half-opened wings, giving the illusion of greater size; at the same time they puff loudly and make a rattling sound with their beaks. These birds are usually the victims of birds of prey. They nest on the ground and the female lays 2 or 3 round, white eggs which are incubated by both parents for thirty days.

VIRGINIAN OWL *(BUBO VIRGINIANUS)*. The size of this owl is similar to that of the royal owl. Its coloring is varied. Almost totally white specimens are found in the polar regions. This owl is found in densely vegetated areas, ranging from Canada to the Magellan Straits. Its staple foods are squirrels, marmots, birds, snakes, lizards, frogs, fish and insects. When many of these birds appear in the same area, their normal amounts of prey are depleted. This owl nests in January or February in the northern hemisphere. It uses the abandoned nests of large birds of prey or makes a very simple nest of its own. The female lays from 1 to 5 white eggs and the young are able to fly after three months.

SNOWY OWL *(NYCTEA SCANTIACA)*. This owl is about 70 cm. in length, with thick, soft, white-banded plumage. It is found in the Arctic and sub-Arctic areas of Eurasia and America. The amount of time this owl spends in a certain area depends on the quantity of lennings and rodents present. These form its diet; it also feeds on Arctic hares and marine birds. It hunts during the day. The snowy owl mates in April and builds a nest of moss and rocks on any small rise of ground. The female lays between 4 and 10 eggs which she incubates for thirty-four days.

SAW WHET OWL *(AEGOLIUS ACADIUS)*. This bird is about 20 cm. in length. It lives in conifer forests in North America, Mexico and Guatemala. It feeds on small mammals such as young squirrels. It breeds between February and April, with the female laying from 3 to 6 white eggs in the abandoned nests of woodpeckers or birds of prey. The incubation period lasts twenty-four days.

SCREECH OWL *(OTUS ASIO)*. This owl is about 15-25 cm. long. It lives in North and Central America in varied habitats. Its diet consists of small mammals and birds, as well as insects. It nests in abandoned nests of woodpeckers, constructing its own nest in open buildings. The female lays from 4 to 8 eggs.

COMMON BARN OWL *(TYTO ALBA)*. The length of this owl is about 40 cm. The upper parts of its body are brownish-yellow and the lower parts are white. It displays a heart-shaped patch on its face. This owl lives in

EAGLE OWL

VIRGINIAN OWL

STRIGIFORMES

SNOWY OWL

SAW WHET OWL

SNOWY OWL

SCREECH OWL

cities, except in northern areas. During the day it remains hidden in attics, bell towers, caves, and inside hollow tree trunks. It does not make a nest, and the female lays from 3 to 7 white, elongated eggs. These owls are beneficial to agriculture as they eat large amounts of harmful rodents; they also eat birds and insects.

FROGMOUTH

The birds of this order exhibit nocturnal or crepuscular habits. Their heads are flattened, the bill is short and the feet are weak. Dully colored, the plumage resembles leaves on the ground. Both sexes display similar features. This order is divided into 5 families with almost 100 species. Among the families we can mention the Caprimulgidae (nightjars), Podargidae (frogmouths), and Steatornithidae (oilbird). Some modern authors include in this order the Trochilidae (hummingbirds) and the Apodidae (swifts), but in this volume these are grouped in the Apodiformes.

FROGMOUTH *(PODARGUS PAPUENSIS)*. This bird is very similar to the nightjar, but with a larger head and mouth. It is found in densely vegetated areas in India and Australia and is mainly active at dusk and at night. During the day it sleeps perched in a tree. This is a slow, seemingly apathetic bird; if the temperature drops too low the bird may enter a lethargic state. Its diet is made up of insects extracted from tree bark, but it also eats small vertebrates. When it has satisfied its hunger, it perches on a tree branch until it is hungry again. During courtship it is more active, the male fighting with other males to win a mate. The pair build a small platform-like nest of twigs, dry grass and roots. The female incubates its 2 to 4 eggs for one month. As the nest is very small, the young leave it after a few days. Both parents feed them, and the young are able to fly in thirty days.

EUROPEAN NIGHTJAR

EUROPEAN NIGHTJAR *(CAPRIMULGUS EUROPAEUS)*. This bird is insectivore par excellence. It measures 28 cm. long. It is gray-brown above and striped below. The European nightjar is found in Europe, Asia and Africa. During the cold season it migrates to southern Africa. During the day nightjars remain on the ground or perched in trees, becoming active at dusk and at night. Flying silently they capture nocturnal insects. These birds do not build nests and the females lay 2 yellowish, brown-spotted eggs on the ground. The eggs are incubated for a period of eighteen days. Nestlings display white down and are fed by both parents; after one month they are able to fly. By popular belief these birds are considered dangerous and it is thought that they suckle goat and sheep milk, and also bring bad luck or are a bad omen.

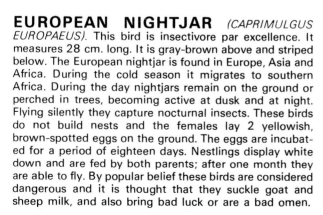

APODIFORMES

The outstanding characteristic of the birds of this order is their weak feet. The bones of the wings are very short but the muscles are very strong and the feathers quite long. The order is divided into Apodidae and Trochilidae.

Apodidae: The birds of this family have a short bill and a large mouth. The plumage is even and dark in color, and their external markings are similar in both sexes. They are insectivores. They nest in trees and in crevices between stones and on buildings. The chicks are helpless when they hatch and are fed by their parents. These birds are among the fastest species as they can reach speeds of up to 300 k.p.h. (185 m.p.h.). They are migratory. In this family we find the swifts and martins, with about 67 species distributed throughout Eurasia, Africa and America.

Trochilidae: These are very small birds, with some species measuring only 5,5 cm. in lenght and weighing 2 grams. Owing to their bright plumage they may be considered "living jewels". These birds can reach speeds of up to 100 k.p.h. (62 m.p.h.), beating their wings about 200 times per second. They can also stand still in the air and fly backwards as hornets do. This family includes 123 genera, 327 species and 668 subspecies. Like insects, they act as pollinizing agents. They feed on pollen and insects found in the corollas of flowers. Most males of these species are poligamous. Their nest of moss and lichens is placed in the fork of a small branch. The females lay 2 very tiny eggs; in the smaller species the eggs barely measure 0,5 cm. Incubation lasts from fourteen to nineteen days. During the winter they migrate to warmer areas and all the species are native to the American continent.

EUROPEAN SWIFT *(APUS APUS).* This bird is 15 cm. long, black in color with a lighter neck. Its tail is short and forked. It is found in Eurasia and Africa in all kinds of terrains, but it thrives in cities. In the spring it migrates to Europe where it remains until mid-summer at which time it returns to southern Africa. It alights on vertical surfaces and should it fall to the ground it is very difficult for the bird to resume flight. Swifts are often mistaken for swallows. The bird feeds on insects which it catches while flying. It nests late in April on cliffs, cornices of buildings, nests abandoned by other birds, and even in trees. The 2 or 3 white eggs are incubated by both parents over a period of twenty days. The young are fully developed in six weeks.

BROWN-THROATED HUMMINGBIRD
ROSE-THROATED HUMMINGBIRD

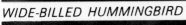

WIDE-BILLED HUMMINGBIRD

These are mainly arboreal birds, their habitat being the thick African, Asian, Central and South American tropical and subtropical jungles. The plumage of the males is metallic green on the upper part of the body, and red or yellow on the lower portions; females are brown or gray. The 1st and 2nd toes are turned backward and the 3th and 4th forward. This order includes about 35 species.

QUETZAL *(PHARAMACHRUS MOCINNO).* The length of this bird is 95 cm. of which 60 cm. belong to the tail. This bird lives alone or in pairs in jungles up to 2,000 m above sea level in tropical America. It makes a deep gallery inside tree trunks hollowed by termites. Females lay 2 bluish eggs and both parents share incubation for a period of eighteen days. This is one of the most beautiful birds, and it is said that if it is captured it expires, but it has been proved otherwise. At present it is zealously protected, and until recently anyone who killed even one quetzal was given the death penalty.

ORANGE-BREASTED HUMMINGBIRD

CORACIIFORMES
KINGFISHER

This is a heterogeneous group of birds with common characteristics regarding the shape of the palate and the position of the toes which are directed forward and joined at the base. The bill is strong and the plumage sparse but colorful. Both sexes share even external features. They live in trees, building their nests inside tree trunks or in burrows. The nestlings are helpless. This order includes 5 families with more than 150 species distributed along the temperate and warm zones all over the world. The families are: Alcedinidae (kingfisher, kookaburra), Meropidae, (bee eaters), Coraciidae (rollers), Bucerotidae (hornbill) and Upupidae (hoopoes).

SACRED KINGFISHER

KINGFISHER *(ALCEDO ATHIS)*. This bird is about 16 cm. in lenght. The upper parts of its body are glossy blue-green and the lower region is brownish-red. The bill is long and pointed. It lives near European, Asian, and African streams, rivers, ponds, and lakes with abundant foliage on their banks. The kingfisher usually awaits quietly on the bank scanning a stream bottom; if a fish is seen, the bird dives to catch it. It also fishes while flying above the surface of the water, diving upon the prey; the kingfisher also likes insect larvae and tadpoles. It flies rapidly in a straight line. Courtship and breeding occur from April to June; at this time they dig a burrow 2 or 3 m. wide and line it with grass and moss. Sometimes they use the burrows of otters. The females lay from 5 to 8 white eggs which are incubated by both parents for a period of fourteen to sixteen days.

SACRED KINGFISHER *(HALCYON SANCTA)*. This bird is about 23 cm. long. The upper portions are blue-green and the neck and lower parts white. It thrives in well-vegetated areas in Australia near rivers or lakes. Its diet is made up of insects and small vertebrates such as fish, amphibians and reptiles. During the summer it usually migrates to southeast Asia.

KOOKABURRA *(DACELO GIGAS)*. This bird resembles the kingfisher. It is 47 cm. long with a large head and bill. It lives in Australia, Tasmania and New Zealand, in open areas with trees, as well as in parks and gardens. It feeds on insects, lizards, and snakes; it also destroys other birds' nests and attacks young fowl. It nests in cavities of trees or digs burrows on the banks of rivers. The female lays from 2 to 4 white eggs, with both parents sharing incubation. At dawn and dusk these birds emit loud calls that resemble laughter.

KOOKABURRA

BEE-EATER

BEE-EATER *(MEROPS APIASTER)*. This bird measures 30 cm. in length, and is equipped with a long, curved bill. The upper parts are brownish-red and yellow; the neck is yellow, the breast and belly green, and the tail emerald green. This is a gregarious bird, found in Europe, Asia, Africa and India, near open fields with trees. It feeds on insects. It nests in a spacious burrow dug in a river bank. The female lays 4 to 6 white eggs. As insectivores, these birds are beneficial to agriculture, but on the other hand, they are harmful for the beekeeping industry.

RED BEE-EATER *(MEROPS NUBICUS)*. The habits of this bird are very similar to those of the common bee-eater, however, this one is larger. Its plumage is quite colorful, with a green head and a reddish body. It lives in arboreal and shrubby plains in tropical Africa.

ROLLER *(CORACIAS GARRULUS)*. The length of this bird is 30 cm. Its head and breast are blue-green, the back brown, and the wings and tail a deep blue. It is found in open arboreal areas in Europe, central, southern Asia, and Africa. Its diet consists of insects, small amphibians and reptiles as well as vegetal substances. It nests in holes in trees or in crevices in old buildings. The female lays 4 or 5 round, white eggs, which she incubates for twenty days.

LILAC-BREASTED ROLLER *(CORACIAS CAUSATUS)*. This bird shares many characteristics with the aforementioned roller. It lives in eastern Africa, in arboreal and shrubby plains. It is very active at dawn and dusk, remaining completely quiet during the warm hours of the day, except when catching insects or small vertebrates.

GREAT HORNBILL *(BUCEROS BICORNIS)*. This is the largest bird in its order, about 130 cm. long. It is black and white in color. A bulge rises from the middle of the head which also extends over the bill. It lives in the Indian and Malaysian tropical jungles. Its diet consists of fruits as well as other birds and reptiles. It nests inside trees hollowed out by termites. The female incubates the 5 or 6 eggs for a month. This bird adapts well to life in captivity.

HOOPOE *(UPUPA EPOPS)*. This bird is 30 cm. long, reddish-brown in color, with striped wings and tail. A crest of erectile feathers characterizes the head. Both sexes display similar features. Hoopoes live in Europe, Asia and Africa in grain-growing, arboreal fields. If they are startled they take shelter in trees. They feed on insects and their larvae, as well as on other invertebrates and small reptiles. They nest in holes in trees or under the eaves of buildings. Females lay from 4 to 7 greenish eggs. During the breeding season these birds emit a foul odor originating from the feces used to line their nests.

RED BEE-EATER   *ROLLER*

ROLLER

GREAT HORNBILL

The birds included in this order are basically forest-dwelling climbers. They have 2 toes pointing forward and 2 backward, all equipped with strong, curved toenails that allow them to climb tree trunks and branches. Their plumage is quite colorful, and sexual differences are not obvious. The wings are moderate in length, and the tail may be long or short, with the feathers varying according to the species. This order is divided into 350 species and 6 families: Picidae (woodpeckers), Ramphastidae (toucans), Indicatoridae (honey guides), Capitonidae (barbets), Bucconidae (puffbirds), and Galbulidae (jacamars).

The Picidae are the best known and most typical family of this order. Woodpeckers are arboreal and especially equipped for climbing trees and branches. Their beaks are strong and the tongue is long and pointed. They are distributed all over the world except Madagascar and Australia. The Ramphastidae are distinguishable by their huge bills. They are predominantly black in color, with bright patches of colors. These birds are found in tropical America, Africa and Asia.

GREEN WOODPECKER *(PICUS VIRIDIS)*.

This bird is about 35 cm. long, usually greenish in color; the rump is yellow and part of the head and feathers around the beak are crimson. It lives in arboreal areas of Europe, Asia Minor and Persia. Its diet consists of ants, insect larvae and at times vegetal substances. Green woodpeckers breed in May and a nest is chiseled in tree trunks. The female lays 6 or 7 eggs which are incubated by both parents for seventeen days.

GREAT SPOTTED WOODPECKER
(DENDROCOPUS MAJOR). This bird is about 35 cm. long with intermingled white and black colors in the plumage; its neck and skullcap are red. It is found in conifer forests in Europe, northern Africa, Asia Minor and Persia, It feeds mainly on ants and xylophague insects, and when nesting it generally uses the abandoned nest of a green woodpecker. Both parents share in incubating the 4 or 6 eggs for seventeen days.

KEE-BILLED TOUCAN *(RHAMPASTOS SUL-FURATUS)*. This bird is approximately 60 cm. long, with a remarkably large green bill. It is found in northern Colombia, and from Mexico to Venezuela. It feeds on fruits, insects and small vertebrates. It nests in holes in trees, and the female lays from 2 to 4 eggs which hatch after seventeen days.

RED-BILLED TOUCAN *(RHAMPASTOS CU-VIERI)*. The face and neck of this bird are white, the skullcap yellow and the rest of the body black. It is found in Venezuelan jungles, Guiana, Brazil, Bolivia and norhern Argentina.

HOOPOE

GREEN WOODPECKER

PICIFORMES

KEE-BILLED TOUCAN

GREAT SPOTTED WOODPECKER

RED-BILLED TOUCAN

PASSERIIFORMES
LYREBIRD

COCK OF THE ROCK

The species of this order include more than half of all living birds. They are usually small. They have 4 toes, 3 directed forward and 1 (the thumb) backward. Anatomical characteristics are similar among the species of this order: the syrinx, vocal mechanism, and the vomer are highly developed, and in all species there are 14 cervical vertebrae. All of the birds of this order build nests. The young hatch helpless and are taken care of by the parents. They are migratory. They thrive all over the world, except in the Arctic and Antarctic areas. This order includes 54 families with more than 5,000 species. Worthy of mention among the families are:

Motacillidae: This family comprises small, elegant birds with a long tail that moves when walking. They live near the water and their diet consists of invertebrates and seeds. This family includes about 70 species distributed world-wide (wagtails).

Menuridae: These birds exhibit sexual dimorphism and possess a beautiful lyre-like tail. They live in densely forested areas in subtropical Australia. (lyrebirds).

Cotingidae: These are showy birds, native to southern, tropical America. They feed on fruits and insects. (cock of the rock).

Hirundinidae: These are small birds, rather dull in color; at times displaying metallic hues. Both sexes share similar features. They make long-range flights and nest in houses or in rocky walls. This family has 80 species spread all over the world except in New Zealand and the Polar regions (common swallows, swifts).

Laniidae: These birds of prey are moderate in size, with a hooked beak. They have gray, white and black plumage. Their external characteristics are similar in both sexes. They generally perch on the upper branches of trees, attacking their victims by surprise and later dropping them into a hawthorn bush. These birds eat small mammals and insects, and when food is scarce they retrieve their cached prey from the bushes. This family includes 75 species, mostly distributed in the Old World. They usually migrate. (shrikes).

Bombycillidae: This birds of this family are native to the northern hemisphere. They are gregarious and migrate during harsh winters. Both sexes share common external characteristics. (waxwings).

PASSERIIFORMES

Muscicapidae: This family includes about 1,000 species which in turn are divided into subspecies, for instance, the Muscicapinae, usually sober in color in both sexes and smaller in the Old species. The tropical species, besides having long tails, are brighter in color. These birds are migratory and insectivorous. Some species exhibit sexual dimorphism, for instance the paradise flycatcher.

The Turnidae subspecies also form part of this family and are distributed all over the world. These are moderate in size, dull in color, and display similar external markings in both sexes. (blackbird).

Nectariniidae: These birds are the hummingbirds of the Old World. Their bill is long and curved. Males have beautiful metallic-hued plumage. They live in pairs or in small flocks. Their diet consists of the nectar of flowers and small invertebrates. This family has about 100 species some of which are migratory. (sunbirds).

Fringillidae: This family includes a large number of species which are difficult to classify. They are distinguished by their short, conical bill and sharp mandibles, fit for peeling seeds and extracting the kermel within. During the nesting season the nestlings are fed with insects. These are social birds, many of which are migratory. Their habitat is extensive. (cardinal, linnet, goldfinch, hawfinch).

Estrildidae: The birds of this family are small grain eaters. They comprise more than 100 species and 15 genera, and are distributed throughout Africa, Asia and Australia. (Gouldian finch, paradise whydah).

Ploceidae: These are small birds with a short, conical bill. Sometimes they show sexual dimorphism. These social birds live in large coveys in varied habitats. They feed on seeds, and during the breeding season consume large amounts of insects. Their nests are built either separately or in groups. This family includes many species distributed throughout Eurasia, Africa and Australia though they have also been introduced into the Americas (weaverbird, etc.)

Sturnidae: The birds of this family are medium-sized, with colorful, metallic-toned plumage. The external markings are similar in both sexes. There are many species in this family, distributed throughout Eurasia, Africa and North America. Some species can mimic sounds and repeat words. (starlings).

COMMON SWALLOW

TREE SWALLOW

HOUSE MARTIN

PASSERIIFORMES

Oriolidae: The males of this family are brightly yellow, red, or black. They are tree-dwellers that feed on fruits and insects. The family is divided into 30 species native to the temperate and warm areas of Eurasia. Some species migrate. (golden oriole).

Paradisaeidae: The beauty of these birds surpasses that of most others; for this reason they are known as "birds of paradise." They display sexual dimorphism and are omnivorous. They live in New Guinea and nearby islands, northern Australia and in the Moluccan Islands. This class has 40 species. (bird or paradise).

Corvidae: These are large, dark birds with similar characteristics in both sexes. Some species make short migratory flights and some are sedentary. They are omnivorous. This family has about 100 species found all over the world. Many species are dependant on man. (chough, crow, mocking bird)

GREAT GRAY SHRIKE

FLYCATCHER

WAXWING

BLACKBIRD

LYREBIRD *(MENURA NOVA-HOLLANDIAE).* This bird is 95 cm. long, grayish-red on its upper parts and light gray in the lower portions, The tail feathers have broad brown and red stripes mixed with finer and white stripes. This bird inhabits eastern Australian forests and is very shy; at the least sign of danger it conceals itself in thick vegetation. It can mimic other birds' calls as well as the bark of a dog, and is capable of fooling even the wiliest hunter. During courtship the males fight violently meeting in certain places to call and perform their mating dances. Their nests are large, and the females lay and incubate there 2 dark spotted gray eggs. They incubate the eggs for seven weeks, and the young abandon the nest late in September. These birds are completely protected by law.

COCK OF THE ROCK *(RUPICOLA RUPICO-LA).* The length of this bird is approximately 30 cm. It is orange in color, except the wings and tail which are dark with white patches. This bird has a semicircular crest that covers the bill. It inhabits rocky areas of tropical America (Venezuela, Guianas and the Amazon River), and feeds on fruits. During the breeding season the males perform elaborate dances and emit sharp calls. The nests are built in rocky hollows, the female laying 2 white eggs. It readily adapts to captivity.

COMMON SWALLOW *(HIRUNDO RUSTI-CA).* This bird measures 20 cm. in length. The upper part of the body is a deep metallic blue, the forehead and neck red, and the lower parts of the body are blue. This swallow is found in grain-growing areas with nearby trees in Eurasia and Africa. It usually perches on telephone wires and dry tree branches. It feeds on insects caught on the wing, and it is beneficial to agriculture because of the large

PASSERIIFORMES

BLUE TITMOUSE

MALACHITE SUNBIRD

amounts of insects it consumes. It only walks on the ground when collecting mud to build its nest, which is lined with feathers. It nests in the northern hemisphere in open structures, barns, cornices, etc. The female lays at least 4 white, spotted eggs and incubation lasts fifteen days. The young are fed by both parents.

TREE SWALLOW (IRIDOPROCNE BICOLOR). This bird is about 15 cm. long. The upper parts of its body are blue-green with metallic hues, and the lower parts are white. It lives in North America and during the winter it migrates to Central America. It feeds on flying insects. It nests in trees, abandoned nests, or in hollows of a dead tree. The female lays from 4 to 7 eggs. This bird migrates to the north in October, and later, to the south. It is commonly seen in the United States.

HOUSE MARTIN (DELICHON URBICA). This bird is slightly smaller than the swallow. The upper parts of the body are metallic black and the lower parts and the rump are white. It lives in Eurasian and African cities and villages as well as in rocky areas. This extremely social bird is a tireless insectivore that spends most of the day catching flying insects. It nests between May and August. The female lays 4 or 5 white eggs which both parents incubate for twelve to fifteen days. Sometimes the female lays a third time in September, but the young die because their flying ability is not developed enough to migrate.

WAXWING (BOMBICILIA GARRULUS). This bird is about 20 cm. long. The upper parts are dark brown and the lower yellowish-brown. It displays a very distinctive crest and the tip of tail is yellow. It is found in northern Eurasian forests of birches and conifers. This bird is very social and peaceful, living in large coveys or small flocks. Its migrations occur at random, depending on the harshness of the winter. It feeds on berries, seeds and insects. It builds its nest of twigs in a tree. The females lay 5 to 7 light blue eggs with dark spots, and the incubation lasts for fourteen days. This bird adapts well in captivity and the sighting of it is believed to be an ill omen, foretelling difficult winters, wars, etc.

GREAT GRAY SHRIKE (LANIUS EXCUBITOR). This bird is about 24 cm. long, with the upper parts gray, the lower white and a black stripe over the eyes. It lives in the northern hemisphere and spends the day perched in a treetop or on telephone wires, scanning the area around him. If the bird spies prey it catches it and carries it to a tree to devour; if the bird eats its fill, it will then place its prey in a hawthorn bush to consume later in harder times. This is a territorial bird that attacks intruders ferociously. Its diet consists of insects, small mammals and birds; it also destroys the nests of other birds. The sedentary species live in pairs; late in the spring both birds build a nest where the female lays from 4 to 6 white-green eggs, which she incubates. The young are constantly fed by their parents, and leave the nest in August.

FLYCATCHER *(TERSIPHONE VIRIDIS).* This bird is about 35 cm. long. The sides of the body are light in color, and the back wings and tail are white. The rest of the body is blue-green with metallic hues. The bill and eyelids are blue, and the colors of the female are duller than the male's. It lives in the greater part of Africa, except in the east and southeast areas. Its migrations are short-range, and it lives in varied habitats: arboreal plains, jungles, and cultivated fields. It feeds on insects and behaves similarly to other birds of the same species. It nests in trees. The female lays 2 or 3 white eggs with red spots.

BLACKBIRD *(TURDUS MERULA).* This bird is about 24 cm. long. The male's coloring is black with a yellow bill and the female is dark brown. It lives in densely forested areas, thickly vegetated stream banks, gardens, etc., in Eurasia and northern Africa. Originally it inhabited forests, being solitary and daring in nature. Since the beginning of this century, however, its conduct has changed and it has become more sedentary, moving to parks and urban gardens. It flushes at the least sign of danger, shrieking loudly. Its diet consists of fruits, worms, insects, mollusks, wastes, etc. The blackbird is a monogamous bird and the female usually builds its nest with the help of the male. They nest in varied sites such as trees, bushes, and even on the ground. The female lays from 3 to 5 eggs which are incubated for fourteen days. The young are able to fly in two weeks.

BLUE TITMOUSE *(PARUS CARRULEUS).* This bird is 12 cm. long, with the upper part of its head, wings and tail blue; the cheeks are white, and the lower parts of

CARDINAL

HAWFINCH

the body yellow. It lives in Europe, northern Africa, Canary Islands and western Asia. The titmouse is a very restless, active bird, constantly moving in forested areas in search of insects, larvae, etc. During the winter it feeds on berries, seeds and fruits. In February it nests in a cavity in the ground or a hole in a tree with a very small entrance; sometimes it uses other birds' abandoned nests, such as those of woodpeckers, which they line with feathers. The female lays from 9 to 13 white eggs with reddish-brown spots. Incubation lasts fourteen days.

MALACHITE SUNBIRD (NECTARINEA FA-MOSA).
This bird is 12 cm. long with green metallic plumage of different hues. It is found throughout a large area of Africa, in the southern Sahara, from Sudan to southern Africa. It feeds on small invertebrates and the nectar of flowers. Its mating season varies according to the latitude of its habitat. It nests in bushes or trees near the ground, and uses the same nest for several years. The eggs are yellow with dark green spots. The female builds the nest and incubates the eggs; the young are fed by the female at first and later by both parents.

CARDINAL (RICHMONDENA CARDINALIS).
The length if this bird is 20 cm. It is entirely red, except the back of the head which is dark. Its habitat is quite varied: woods, bushy areas, cultivated fields, gardens, etc. It feeds on seeds and insects. It adapts well to life in captivity. The cardinal mates in the spring and summer and nests in trees. The female lays from 3 to 5 white or light green eggs with red spots. Incubation lasts fifteen days and the nestlings are fed by both parents.

HAWFINCH (COCCOTHRAUSTES COCCO-THRAUSTES).
This bird is 18 cm. long, and possesses a large bill, a yellowish-brown head, and dark neck. The lower parts of the body are deep pink, the back and the wings light pink, with light stripes on them. It lives in pairs or small flocks in forests, parks, and gardens in Eurasia and northern Africa. Berries, egg yolk, flower buds, fruits and insects are its staple foods. This bird mates in April, making a nest with dry twigs and lining it with grasses and hair. The female incubates the 4 to 6 eggs for twelve days, and the male feeds its mate. The parents feed their young on insects, and after two weeks the nestlings follow their parents wherever they go until late August when they become independent.

GOLDFINCH

GOULDIAN FINCH

PASSERIIFORMES

PARADISE WHYDAH

BULLFINCH *(PYRRHULA PYRRHULA)*. This bird is about 16 cm. in length, with the upper part of the head black in color, the sides gray, the wings and tail black, and the rump white; the male has a red breast, and the female's is reddish-brown. It is found in pairs or in small flocks in wooded areas in southern Europe (northern Spain, Apennines, and Balkans), and northern Asia up to Japan. Its diet consists of seeds and berries, the young feeding on insects. This is a monogamous bird and the female lays twice a year in April and in June. While the female is incubating the eggs, the male feeds her. The bullfinch's migrations are short depending on the availability of food substances.

GOLDFINCH *(CARDUELIS CARDUELIS)*. This bird is about 12 cm. in length. Its head is red, black and white. The body is ocher, the wings black with a wide yellow band. The rump is white and the tail black. Plumage is similar in both sexes. It lives in open areas with occasional trees, in cultivated fields, or in gardens. Its song is very pleasant. It feeds on seeds, thistles, sunflowers, etc.; during the nesting season the young are fed with insects. The goldfinch begins to nest in May and the female can lay for a second time in July. The nest is built in the uppermost branches of trees where the female lays 4 or 5 white-greenish eggs with reddish spots. Both parents incubate the eggs for fifteen days. Twenty days after hatching the young are fully plumed and leave the nest, following their parents; in August the family separates.

GOULDIAN FINCH *(POEPHILA GOULDIAE)*. This bird is about 12 cm. long. The upper parts of the male's body are green; the head is red and the neck black. The breast is blue and the belly yellow. It lives in tropical, wooded areas of Australia. Due to the beauty of its plumage, this bird is greatly priced for its decorative value. It feeds on seeds, alighting on grass shoots, and very seldomly walking on bare ground. This bird nests in flocks from February to June. It builds its nest in bushes or trees, and the female lays about 7 eggs, which are incubated by both parents. The young birds are fed with insects and after three weeks they leave the nest.

PARADISE WHYDAH *(STEGANURA PARADI-SAEA)*. This bird is 38 cm. long including the tail. During courtship the male's head, wings and tail are black, the neck and belly brownish-red and the breast red. It lives in small coveys in South Africa, near arboreal or brushy plains. Its diet consists of seeds and insects. The female is parasitic and does not build a nest, laying her eggs in the nests of Estrildidae. The male molts its tail feathers when the breeding season is over.

STARLING

PASSERIIFORMES

SUPERB STARLING

BIRD OF PARADISE *(PARADISEA RAGGIANA).*
This bird is about 45 cm. long. The male is usually reddish-brown with a yellow head and bright green neck; it
displays two colorful yellowish-red fans on both sides of
its body. It lives in New Guinea and nearby islands, near
densely vegetated areas. This bird feeds on fruits. During
the mating season the males gather together in the branches of a tree and perform a mating dance, exhibiting their
plumage and calling aloud. Females are soon attracted by
their performances. This bird has been relentlessly hunted
for its plumage. At present the hunting of the bird of paradise is very restricted as it was on the brink of extinction. It
adapts well in captivity and can be seen in many zoos. It
nests in trees and the female incubates 2 eggs.

MOCKINGBIRD *(GARRULUS GLANDARIUS).*
The length of this bird is about 32 cm. Its body is reddish-
gray with a white rump. The tail and wings are dark and
the two middle feathers of the tail black and blue. It lives
in conifer forests in Eurasia and northern Africa. This
bird usually scans the surrounding area carefully, warning
other inhabitants of the forest with his loud cry if danger
approaches. The mockingbird is omnivorous and feeds on
fruits, berries and insects; it also destroys other birds'
nests in order to eat the eggs or the young. During the fall
it stores acorns by burying them in the ground or in nests
of other birds; in this way it helps to disseminate oak
trees. It nests in trees or bushes in mid-April; the female
lays and incubates 5 or 6 eggs for a period of sixteen days.
The fledglings develop rapidly enough to leave the nest
after one month.

MAGPIE *(PICA PICA).* This bird is 42 cm. long. Its
plumage is mainly black with metallic overtones; the outer
shoulder and under plumage are white. It is found in cultivated fields and wooded areas in Eurasia, northeastern
Africa and North America. This bird is harmful to other
species because it destroys a great amount of their nests.
It also devastates grain-growing areas, especially corn
fields. It is omnivorous, also feeding on insects, crickets,
grasshoppers, small birds and rodents. In April or May
both parents spend a month building a high-placed nest.
The female incubates the 4 to 8 pale green, brown
spotted, elongated eggs for eighteen days. The young stay
in the nest twenty-four days, after which they leave it,
remaining with their parents for some time.

BIRD OF PARADISE

GOLDEN ORIOLE

PASSERIIFORMES

CHOUGH

JAY

MAGPIE

ICONOGRAPHY: Salmer - X. Palaus - Geocolor.

COLLECTION

SAFARI Color®

MAMMALS	84-7424-009-3
BIRDS	84-7424-082-4
AMPHIBIANS - FISH - REPTILES	84-7424-080-8
INVERTEBRATES	84-7424-077-8
IN THE AMERICAN CONTINENT	84-7424-076-X

Printed in Spain  GEOCOLOR®

impreso en IGOL. industria gráfica BARCELONA- D.L. 15.370-B.

Potter Park Zoological Society
1301 S. Pennsylvania
Lansing, Michigan 48912